Contents

Sentence punctuation

Remember

Sentences start with a **capital letter** and end with a **full stop**.
Proper nouns (or names) also start with a capital letter.

An explorer called Christopher Columbus discovered America.

Try it

1 Add the missing **capital letter** and **full stop** on each line.

The tree was creaking in the storm we thought a branch might fall.

Jess waited for me by the gate she wanted to hear my news.

He ran home as fast as he could megan followed him.

Let's go fishing my friend Ravi wants to come with us.

Imogen kicked the ball and scored the crowd all cheered.

2 Rewrite each line, adding in the **capital letters** and **full stops**.

the city of washington is in america it is named after george washington

_____

_____

queen victoria married prince albert in 1840 he died in december 1861

_____

_____

sir francis drake was a famous english sailor he lived in the reign of queen elizabeth I.

_____

_____

Sentence practice

Write a sentence about a teacher. Use at least <u>three</u> **proper nouns**.

_____

Sentence types

All **sentences** start with a capital letter. **Statements** and **commands** usually end with a full stop, **questions** end with a question mark, and **exclamations** end with an exclamation mark.

What a noise that is!   Harry is playing the drums.

What is that terrible noise?   Tell him to stop.

Try it

1 Complete each sentence with the correct **punctuation mark**.

Are you coming to see the film ___ It starts at five o'clock ___

What a great idea that is ___ Meet me outside the cinema ___

Did you see the match on Saturday ___ It was a great game ___

What a result it was ___ Do you know who scored the winner ___

I have fixed the clock ___ What shall I do with it now ___

How clever of you that is ___ Show me how you did it ___

2 Write a **question** or an **exclamation** to follow each sentence. Use the correct punctuation.

Did it rain on your holiday? What _____

What lovely flowers they are! What _____

He gave all his money to charity. How _____

I can't reach the jar on the top shelf. Can _____

I am having an ice cream. Do _____

Sentence practice

Write <u>three</u> sentences about going camping. Use <u>three</u> different types of sentence.

_____

_____

_____

Noun phrases

You can add **adjectives** to a **noun** to say more about it. This makes a longer **noun phrase**. You can also make a longer noun phrase by adding some detail after the noun.

man (noun)   a tall, thin man (noun phrase)

sword (noun)   a sword with a wooden handle (noun phrase)

Try it

1   Complete each noun phrase using **adjectives** and descriptive details.

the clown's _____ _____ shoes

Grandad's _____ _____ tie

the _____ _____ girl in

_____

my _____ slippers with _____

the queen's _____ _____ dress with _____

the _____ _____ puppy with the _____ eyes

2   Use **adjectives** to complete these sentences.

The wood was _____ and _____ .

The car looked _____ and _____ .

The clouds were _____ and _____ .

The woman was _____ and _____ .

The prince was _____ but _____ .

The dragon was _____ but _____ .

Sentence practice

Write a sentence using a longer **noun phrase** to describe a cat.

_____

_____

Using 'a' or 'an'

Remember

You can use the words 'a' and 'an' before nouns and noun phrases. You use 'a' before words beginning with a **consonant** sound and 'an' before words beginning with a **vowel** sound.

a <u>d</u>iary   a <u>t</u>rain ticket   an <u>e</u>nvelope   an <u>o</u>ld watch

Try it

1 Write 'a' or 'an' before each noun.

_____ duck   _____ owl   _____ eagle   _____ swan

_____ inkpot   _____ stamp   _____ address   _____ postcard

_____ scarf   _____ umbrella   _____ jacket   _____ hood

_____ toaster   _____ iron   _____ apron   _____ kettle

_____ arm   _____ elbow   _____ hand   _____ thumb

_____ nose   _____ ear   _____ eye   _____ mouth

2 Complete the sentences by adding 'a' or 'an' before each noun.

Do you want _____ cake, _____ ice cream, _____ orange or _____ apple?

I need _____ egg, _____ tomato, _____ onion and _____ red pepper.

I saw _____ oak tree, _____ birch, _____ elm and _____ willow.

Is _____ ant _____ insect or _____ reptile?

_____ minute is shorter than _____ hour but longer than _____ second.

The circus had _____ juggler, _____ acrobat, _____ clown and _____ amazing tightrope walker.

There was once _____ beautiful princess, _____ ugly prince, _____ evil monster and _____ clever witch.

Sentence practice

Complete this sentence by adding a list of <u>four</u> animals. Use the word 'an' <u>two</u> times.

At the zoo I saw _____

Commas in lists

Remember

Commas are used to separate items in a list of words or noun phrases. There is no comma before the last item. You use the word 'and' (or the word 'or') instead.

It was a beautiful garden with tall blossom trees, neat hedges, glittering fountains, brightly coloured flowers and soft green grass.

Try it

1 Add the missing **comma** or commas to each sentence.

She felt in her coat pocket and found a green hair ribbon two squares of chocolate a clean tissue and her lost glove.

People were chatting buying popcorn and finding their seats.

The servants cleaned the windows polished the silver swept the floors and dusted the furniture.

Squirrels have grey fur bushy tails pointed ears and sharp claws.

Do you want a fried egg a slice of toast a banana or a bowl of porridge?

2 Complete each sentence by adding <u>three</u> more **noun phrases**. Use the correct **punctuation**.

Inside the room was a comfy chair _____

_____

He decorated the cake with two colours of icing _____

_____

The monster ate six red buses _____

_____

Sentence practice

Write a sentence to say what someone in a story was wearing. Include a list of <u>four</u> **noun phrases**.

_____

Apostrophes for possession

Remember

Apostrophes are used in **contractions** or shortened forms of words. Apostrophes are also used with the letter '**s**' to show that something belongs to someone or something. The apostrophe shows possession.

Dad's toolbox   the dog's kennel

Try it

1 Underline the word that has an **apostrophe** to show that something belongs to someone.

I'll put the folders on the teacher's desk.

That's the fisherman's boat over there.

There's a pigeon sitting on the scarecrow's hat.

I can't find the dog's lead anywhere.

Mum's taken Dad's car to the garage.

The boy's arm is in a sling because he's broken it.

2 Rewrite each phrase using an **apostrophe** to show possession.

the easel belonging to the artist   _____

the nest belonging to the bird   _____

the burrow belonging to the rabbit   _____

the stripes of a tiger   _____

the wings of an owl   _____

the surface of the Earth   _____

Sentence practice

Write a sentence about something that belongs to a pirate. Use an **apostrophe**.

_____

_____

Using adjectives to compare

You can use **adjectives** to compare things. With short adjectives, add the **suffixes** –er and –est.

fast   faster   fastest

With longer adjectives, use the words '**more**' and '**most**'.

comfortable   more comfortable   most comfortable

Try it

1 Complete the table of **adjectives**. Some have been done for you.

Adjective	–er or 'more'	–est or 'most'
smooth	smoother	
fierce		
hungry		
important		most important
famous	more famous	
surprising		

2 Complete each sentence with the correct form of the **adjective**.

This snake is _____ than that one.   (dangerous)

Is this the _____ star in the sky?   (bright)

Simon is the _____ boy I know.   (happy)

It was the _____ sunset.   (beautiful)

This story is _____ than your last one.   (good)

Sentence practice

Write a sentence using **adjectives** to compare two fairground rides.

_____

Conjunctions

Remember

A **conjunction** is a joining word. Conjunctions are used to join together two ideas or two sentences to make one longer sentence.

The little girl was worried because the cottage door was open.

Try it

1 Choose the best **conjunction** from the box to complete each sentence. Use each conjunction only <u>once</u>.

> **and   that   but   when   if   or**

I went swimming for the first time _____ I was four years old.

They tried to go on _____ the bad weather forced them back.

She opened the cupboard _____ found the cooking pot.

I might go fishing _____ I might swim in the sea.

You can come on the trip _____ you get here on time.

The doctor told him _____ his wrist was broken.

2 Complete each sentence using the **conjunction** in **bold**.

The snowman melted **when** _____

The day was almost over **but** _____

I was hurrying to catch the bus **when** _____

The sheep will escape **if** _____

I'm glad **that** _____

Rachel won the prize **because** _____

Sentence practice

Write <u>two</u> sentences about the weather today. Use <u>two</u> different **conjunctions**.

_____

_____

Conjunctions to show time

Conjunctions such as 'when', 'before', 'after' and 'while' help to show <u>when</u> events happen.

Queen Isabella ate a slice of cake before she returned to the palace.

Try it

1 Choose the best **conjunction** to complete each sentence.

I finished my book _____ I went to sleep.   (before after while)

Switch off the computer _____ you have finished.   (while before when)

I packed my bag _____ Mum was waiting.   (after while until)

Wash your hands _____ you clean the hamster cage.   (until as after)

They searched the wood _____ it was dark.   (as until while)

There was not a sound _____ we crept up the path.   (after as before)

2 Complete each sentence using the **conjunction** in **bold**.

The old man smiled <u>**when**</u>

The thieves broke in <u>**while**</u>

She closed the door <u>**before**</u>

We played outside <u>**until**</u>

I was tired <u>**after**</u>

I heard the phone ring <u>**as**</u>

Sentence practice

Write <u>three</u> sentences about what you do when you get home from school. Use <u>three</u> different **conjunctions**.

_____

_____

_____

Conjunctions to show cause

Remember

Conjunctions such as 'because', 'as' and 'since' are used to show the cause or reason for an event. They help to tell you <u>why</u>.

I was late for school because <u>my alarm clock did not go off</u>.

Try it

1 Underline the cause or reason for the action or event in each sentence. Circle the **conjunction**.

She stayed in bed all day because she was ill.

I left the last sandwich as I don't really like cheese.

We had to turn back since all the roads were blocked.

School will be closed on Monday as it is a holiday.

She went to look in the fridge because she felt hungry.

You can go out to play since you have finished your work.

He was lost so he looked at his map.

2 Complete each sentence by adding a cause or reason next to the **conjunction** in **bold**.

We can't plant the vegetables outside **as** _____

The boat will not float **because** _____

We couldn't cross the bridge **since** _____

We went to the pet shop **because** _____

_____ **so** he hid in the cupboard.

I shall wear my wellington boots **as** _____

Sentence practice

Write a sentence to say why you could not do your homework. Use a **conjunction**.

_____

Revision 1

1 Add the missing **suffix** to complete the **adjective** in each noun phrase.

a wise and power_____ leader

a faith_____ old dog

a brave and fear_____ explorer

a refreshing but taste_____ drink

2 Complete each sentence with an **adjective** that starts with **un–**.

Katie thought the punishment was _____.

Dad was annoyed because my bedroom was _____.

They did not like the _____ smell.

We were _____ to lose the game.

3 Write a **verb** to complete each sentence. Use the correct **verb form** and check the **tense**.

The king's voice boomed as he _____ into the room.

I lay on the floor and _____ under the bed.

Police are _____ for the bank robbers.

Flora knew that someone was _____ at her.

4 Rewrite each sentence so that each **noun** is a **plural**.

We saw the horse and pony in the stable.

_____

The lorry took the box to the shop.

_____

The teacher took the child to the garden.

_____

5 Rewrite each sentence using **capital letters** in the correct places.

sir edmund hillary climbed mount everest in may 1953.

_____

You will find moorton primary school on upland road in newtown.

_____

Next friday tom and i will go to Leeds to see Matt.

_____

6 Rewrite the underlined words as a **contraction** using an **apostrophe**.

I <u>have not</u> seen the film yet. _____

It <u>does not</u> seem fair. _____

<u>She is</u> late again. _____

He <u>is not</u> coming. _____

<u>It is</u> my birthday today. _____

7 Here is the start of a story. It is missing **full stops** and **capital letters**. Add them in.

there was once a frail old woman she lived all alone with her two

dogs in a little house there was never much to eat because the old

woman had no money

8 Here is part of a thank-you note. Add the missing **sentence punctuation**.

Thank you for the birthday present what a brilliant surprise it was

I really wanted a new camera because I broke mine did you know

Writing task 1

My favourite meal

Write about the most delicious meal you have ever eaten. Choose an idea from the pictures, or use one of your own. Your task is to describe the meal and to make it sound mouth-watering.

Before you start writing, think about:

● how to describe the meal to someone who has not seen or tasted it

● how it looks, smells and tastes

● why it is your favourite

Use this space to write down some ideas.

Remember

- Write in sentences.
- Use correct punctuation.
- Check your work carefully.

My favourite meal

Adverbs to show how

Remember

Adverbs give extra detail about the **verb** or action in a sentence.
Adverbs can tell you how the action is performed.
Many adverbs end with **–ly**, but some do not.

She carried the jelly slowly. The jelly wobbled
slightly. Everyone stood still.

Try it

1 Underline the **adverb** in each sentence.

Everyone waited nervously for the show to begin.

The play was great and all the children sang well.

Poor Ben tripped and fell awkwardly on the stage.

The actors bowed proudly at the end of the show.

Ms Wilkinson thanked the children for working hard.

The children listened politely to her speech.

2 Rewrite each sentence below, adding a suitable **adverb** to say how the
action happened.

The parrot squawked. _____

He shuffled his feet. _____

The cat landed on the grass. _____

She gripped the rope. _____

The harvest was gathered. _____

The boy whispered. _____

Sentence practice

Write two sentences about the start of a snowstorm. Use an **adverb** in
each sentence.

_____

_____

Adverbs to show time and place

Remember

Adverbs tell you more about the **verb** or action in a sentence. Some adverbs tell you where or when the action happens.

Mr Magico the magician will appear soon.   (when)
Mr Magico the magician will appear here.   (where)

Try it

1 Underline the **adverb** that says when or where each event happened.

There was a bank raid yesterday.

The police arrived and parked outside.

They cleared the area first.

The police began to search everywhere.

A second police car arrived afterwards.

They found the stolen money nearby.

2 Add an **adverb** from the box to each sentence to say <u>when</u> the action happens. Use each adverb only <u>once</u>.

soon   today   shortly   now   later   immediately

The train will arrive _____.

We went to the library _____.

I can play football with you _____.

He dealt with the problem _____.

We are leaving for the station _____.

Let's stop for lunch _____.

Sentence practice

Write a sentence using **adverbs** to say where <u>and</u> when a talent show will begin.

Prepositions to show place

Prepositions tell you where something is in relation to something else.

The runaway tractor rattled under the bridge.

The tractor stopped on the grass by the duck pond.

Try it

1 Underline the **preposition** or prepositions in each sentence.

The wind blew the woman's hat off her head.

It flew through the air and it landed in a tree.

The woman saw it fall from the branch and drop on to the wall.

Then the hat fell over the wall and landed beside the bins.

The woman ran into the garden and found her hat by a rubbish bag.

2 Choose a **preposition** from the box to complete each sentence.
Use each preposition only <u>once</u>.

above	at	beneath	inside	under
across	behind	down	on	up

The goblin lived _____ the bridge.

There was a sign _____ the shop.

The woman climbed _____ the mountain.

Oliver is _____ Mary's house.

They sat _____ the beach _____ a palm tree.

He found the treasure _____ the cave _____ a large rock.

She ran _____ the road and hurried _____ Blake Street.

Sentence practice

Write a sentence about where you saw Stefan's dog. Use <u>two</u>
prepositions.

Prepositions to show time

Remember

Prepositions can also show when an event happened. The preposition is followed by a **noun** or **noun phrase** to make a prepositional phrase.

The ghost appeared after breakfast.

The ghost appeared on Sunday morning.

Try it

1 Add a **preposition** from the box to each sentence to show when the event happens. Use each preposition only <u>once</u>.

> **at   before   during   for   in   until**

Snow fell _____ the night.

They waited _____ two hours.

The old man woke up _____ dawn.

I will be with you _____ a moment.

Mum always goes for a run _____ work.

We were best friends _____ the argument.

2 Complete the phrase after the **preposition** in **bold** to say when each event takes place.

I must visit Gran **on** _____

He will be here **in** _____

The clock began to chime **at** _____

We played football **for** _____

You must finish the story **before** _____

The competition is open **until** _____

Sentence practice

Write a sentence saying when you do P.E. Use at least <u>one</u> preposition.

Inverted commas in direct speech

In **direct speech**, **inverted commas** (or speech marks) are used to show which words are spoken. The inverted commas go at the start and the end of the spoken words.

"My name is Mark 6," said the robot.
"That's a strange name," said Charlie.

Try it

1 Underline the spoken words in each sentence. Then add the missing **inverted commas**.

I don't like sprouts, muttered Vicky.

Nonsense, they are good for you, said Mum.

But they are green and smelly, moaned Vicky.

They are vegetables, replied Mum. Of course they are green.

I'm not going to eat them, insisted Vicky grumpily.

We will see about that, said Mum firmly.

2 Rewrite these sentences with the **inverted commas** in the correct place.

I shall gobble you up, said the troll.

_____

That's a lovely idea, said Mrs Haines.

_____

I will visit my friend the snake, said the monkey.

_____

Sentence practice

Write a sentence using **direct speech** to follow the sentence below.

"Where are you going with that basket of delicious cakes?" asked the wolf.

_____

Punctuation in direct speech

In **direct speech**, you usually put a **comma** at the end of the spoken words. Sometimes you need to use a question mark or exclamation mark instead. This end punctuation always goes inside the **inverted commas**.

"Shall I make them walk the plank_?_" asked Pirate Pete.

Try it

1 Add the **inverted commas** in the correct place.

Can you show me a magic trick? asked George.

Don't make a noise, warned Riham.

How clever of me this is! laughed the old lady.

The journey will take many days, explained the captain of the ship.

Will someone fetch me a drink of water? the old man asked.

Go away! yelled Sam.

2 Rewrite each sentence adding **inverted commas** and the missing end **punctuation**.

Are you feeling better asked the doctor.

_____

What beautiful colours they are exclaimed Jude.

_____

Empty your pockets demanded the wizard.

_____

Sentence practice

Alfie asks his mum if he can go to Zainab's party. Write his question and her answer as **direct speech**, using the correct **punctuation**.

_____

Verbs: past tense

Remember

To write a **verb** in the **past tense**, you often add **–ed** to the present tense verb. However, some verbs do not follow this pattern.

We collect our tickets.   We collect<u>ed</u> our tickets.
We find our seats.   We f<u>ou</u>nd our seats.

In the past tense, the **progressive** or **–ing form** of verbs uses the words '**was**' and '**were**'.

Music is playing.   Music was playing.

Try it

1 Write the underlined **verbs** in the **past tense**.

She <u>writes</u> a letter and then she <u>posts</u> it.   _____ _____

The earth <u>shakes</u> when the giant <u>jumps</u>.   _____ _____

I <u>carry</u> on until I <u>come</u> to a crossroads.   _____ _____

Dad <u>cooks</u> some porridge and we <u>eat</u> it.   _____ _____

We <u>drag</u> the rubbish outside and <u>throw</u> it away.   _____ _____

2 Write each sentence in the **past tense**, using the **progressive** or **–ing form** of the verb.

Rapunzel washed her hair. _____

The young man strolled along. _____

The queen counted her money. _____

I found my homework difficult. _____

The dog ate the cake. _____

She pointed at something. _____

Sentence practice

Write a sentence using the **verbs** 'meet' and 'speak' in the **past tense**.

_____

Verbs: perfect form

You can use the **perfect form** of **verbs** to write about things that have happened in the past and are still happening now. To do this you put the 'helper' verb '**has**' or '**have**' before the main verb.

It has <u>rained</u> all week.   I have <u>played</u> games.
Dad has <u>finished</u> his book. We have <u>been</u> to a museum.

Try it

1 Add '**has**' or '**have**' to complete these sentences, which all use the perfect form of the verb.

I _____ packed my suitcase.

We _____ listened to the weather forecast.

Mum _____ planned the route.

Dad _____ found the deckchairs and the surfboards.

My brother Aiden _____ watered the plants.

We _____ made a picnic. Now we are ready to go!

2 Rewrite each sentence using the **perfect form** of the **verb**.

They waited for two hours.   _____

We painted the front door.   _____

She washed her hands.   _____

He ate all the chocolate cake.   _____

I saw Kelly today.   _____

Sentence practice

Write <u>three</u> sentences about things you have done today, using the **perfect form** of the **verbs**.

So far today, _____

_____

Nouns with suffixes

Try it

1 Add a **suffix** from the box to make each word into a new **noun**.

–er   –ation   –ship   –ness   –ment   –ing

defend	_____	shred	_____
pay	_____	punish	_____
friend	_____	member	_____
invite	_____	tempt	_____
weak	_____	foolish	_____
warn	_____	paint	_____

2 Use a **suffix** to complete each **noun** in these sentences.

The soft_____ of the pillow made Jo forget about her tired_____ .

The report_____ said the show was great entertain_____ .

The juggle_____ dropped the hoops, to everyone's amuse_____ .

The settle_____ was made up of six build_____ .

Morgan's one weak_____ is his forgetful_____ .

The work_____ and the manage_____ came to an agree_____ .

Sentence practice

Add a **suffix** to the word 'excite' to make a **noun**. Write a sentence using the new word.

_____

_____

Nouns with prefixes

Remember

A **prefix** is a group of letters added to the start of a word to make a new word. Some **nouns** are formed by adding a prefix to a word.

supermarket   interview

Try it

1 Add a **prefix** from the box to make each word into a new **noun**.

| inter–   super–   sub–   anti–   auto–   over– |

_____heading   _____net

_____viewer   _____mobile

_____graph   _____star

_____woman   _____way

_____coat   _____pilot

_____septic   _____time

2 Complete each noun by adding the missing **prefix**.

| inter–   super–   sub–   anti–   auto–   over–   re– |

When we went to the theatre we had an ice cream in the _____val.

Spiderman is a _____hero because he has _____powers.

The _____marine sank down to the ocean floor.

After you wash your hands, _____apply the _____bacterial cream.

I read Nelson Mandela's _____biography.

The painter put on his _____alls before he started to paint the ceiling.

Sentence practice

Write a sentence to explain the meaning of the **noun** 'superstore'.

_____

Revision 2

1 Rewrite each sentence, adding a suitable **adverb** to show how the action is peformed.

"Come here!" Mum shouted.

_____

Tears trickled down his face.

_____

The children ran into the playground.

_____

2 Add a <u>different</u> time **conjunction** to complete each sentence.

The boy hurried home _____ he saw it was getting dark.

A fox appeared _____ the rabbit was dozing in the sun.

The children played on the swings _____ it was time for tea.

I always brush my teeth _____ I go to school.

3 Why is the word '**an**' used in the sentence below?

Do you want a strawberry tart or <u>an</u> ice cream?

_____

_____

4 Rewrite each sentence with **proper nouns** in place of the underlined nouns and noun phrases.

<u>The man</u> went to <u>the station</u> to get a ticket to <u>town</u>.

_____

<u>The boy</u> invited everyone to the disco at <u>his school</u>.

_____

<u>The twins</u> went to <u>the theme park</u>.

_____

5 Complete each sentence by giving a reason. Use a <u>different</u> **conjunction** for each one.

I wouldn't want a dragon for a pet _____

I would rather have a dog _____

6 Add **adjectives** or descriptive phrases to make these nouns into longer **noun phrases**.

the bin   _____

the lion   _____

the suitcase   _____

the table   _____

7 *Mum walks into the kitchen. Jake has dropped a cheesecake on the floor. It has made a mess.*

Write an **exclamation** Mum might say.

_____

Write a **question** Mum might ask.

_____

Write a **command** Mum might say.

_____

8 Write <u>three</u> descriptive sentences about a boat in a storm. Use **adjectives**, **adverbs**, **prepositions** and **conjunctions** to add detail.

_____

_____

_____

Writing task 2

An exciting journey

Write an email to a friend about an exciting journey you have been on or can imagine. Choose an idea from the pictures, or use one of your own. Your task is to tell your friend all about the journey and to explain what made it so exciting.

Before you start writing, think about:

- how to describe the journey
- why it was exciting
- what you saw and what happened

Use this space to write down some ideas.

Remember

- Write in sentences.
- Use correct punctuation.
- Check your work carefully.

An exciting journey

Dear _____

_____

_____

_____

_____

_____

_____

_____

_____

_____

_____

_____

_____

_____

_____

_____

_____

_____

Clauses and phrases

Remember

A **phrase** is a group of words that go together but do <u>not</u> make a complete sentence.

in the woods   one cold night

A **clause** is a group of words that go together and include a **verb**. Some clauses are complete sentences – they make sense on their own. These are **main clauses**.

snow began to fall   he heard an owl

Try it

1 Tick the correct box to show whether each group of words is a **clause** or a **phrase**.

	clause	phrase
in the classroom	☐	☐
the room was quiet	☐	☐
the bell rang	☐	☐
the boy with a cheeky grin	☐	☐
Aruna rushed in	☐	☐

2 Add a **clause** to these **phrases** to complete each sentence.

_____ at the traffic lights in Hope Street.

_____ on a comfortable chair by the fireplace.

_____ in a maze of tunnels.

_____ down the corridor.

_____ with sharp green eyes.

Sentence practice

Write a sentence about a juggler, using <u>one</u> **clause** and <u>one</u> added **phrase**.

Subordinate clauses

Remember

You can use a **conjunction** to add another clause to a **main clause**.

Archie screamed <u>because</u> he hated spiders.

This extra clause is a **subordinate clause**. A subordinate clause usually starts with a conjunction. It is <u>not</u> a complete sentence and does not make sense on its own.

Try it

1 Underline the **subordinate clause** in the sentence.

The house was empty when the family moved in.

It began to rain while we were on the mountain.

The skeletons rattled when they danced.

Rover lay on the floor as the ground shook.

I was tired before we reached the top of the hill.

The room was cosy although it was cold outside.

2 Complete the **subordinate clause** after each **main clause**, using the conjunction in **bold**.

My sister laughed **when** _____

The pirates watched **as** _____

The moon rose **while** _____

Bake the cake in the oven **until** _____

She tried to grab the rope **before** _____

Sentence practice

Write a sentence about a thief, using a **main clause** and a **subordinate clause**.

_____

Paragraphs: non-fiction

A **paragraph** is a group of **sentences** that go together because they have one main idea or theme.

Exercise helps you to stay fit and healthy. It is important that you do some exercise every day. The more you use your body, the better it works.

In non-fiction texts, **sub-headings** can show what a paragraph is about. The paragraph above could have the sub-heading 'Exercise'.

Try it

1. Here is the first sentence of a **paragraph**. Write <u>three</u> more sentences for this paragraph.

   It is important to stay safe in the sun. _____

   _____

   _____

   _____

2. Here are some **sub-headings** for a report on materials. Write <u>two</u> sentences for each one.

   Wood _____

   _____

   Glass _____

   _____

   Plastic _____

   _____

Sentence practice

Write the first sentence for a **paragraph** about sheep in a report on farm animals.

_____

Paragraphs: stories and accounts

Remember

In stories and accounts, you start a new **paragraph** for a new event or a change in time or place. **Adverbs** or **prepositional phrases** at the start of paragraphs can help to show these changes.

On Monday morning, Doctor Foster went to Gloucester.

Outside the station, he fell in a puddle.

Immediately, the water was up to his middle.

Try it

1 Here are the main events in a story. Underline the **adverbs** and **prepositional phrases** that show time or place.

One sunny day, Hare and Tortoise had a race.

Soon, Hare was way ahead.

At the top of the hill, Hare stopped for a sleep.

Eventually, Tortoise passed Hare.

After a long time, Hare woke up.

At the finishing line, Tortoise was waiting for Hare.

2 Imagine you are writing a story about a journey. Write **adverbs** and **phrases** for the start of **paragraphs** to show changes in time and place.

On Saturday,	**Time**

At the station,	**Place**

Sentence practice

Write the first **paragraph** of your story about a journey. Write on a new piece of paper.

Root words

Many words are formed by adding a **prefix** and/or a **suffix** to a **root word**. The root word is the original word without any prefixes or suffixes.

disagreement = dis agree ment

prefix   root word   suffix

Try it

1 Find the **root word** hidden in each of these longer words.

refreshments _____

ownership _____

enjoyable _____

unavoidable _____

reawaken _____

international _____

2 Write <u>two</u> words that you can make by adding a **prefix** and/or a **suffix** to each root word.

build _____ _____

happy _____ _____

tidy _____ _____

friend _____ _____

place _____ _____

lead _____ _____

Sentence practice

Add a **prefix** and a **suffix** to the root word 'cover'. Use the new word in a sentence.

Word families

Try it

1 Draw a line to match each word to another word in the same **word family**.

press	circus
circle	solution
equal	medicine
question	pressure
solve	equate
medical	request

2 Look at the <u>three</u> words in the **word family**. Write the **root word** of each family.

design   signature   signal   _____

cyclist   bicycle   cyclone   _____

actor   action   react   _____

fruity   fruitful   grapefruit   _____

natural   supernatural   unnatural   _____

opposite   opponent   opposition   _____

sensation   sensible   sensitive   _____

Sentence practice

Write a sentence using another word from the same **word family** as 'terror'.

Word classes

Remember

Words can be **nouns**, **verbs**, **adjectives** or **adverbs**. Some words have more than one meaning and belong to more than one **word class**. You need to look at the rest of the sentence to work out what the word means and what type of word it is.

The horse is fit and well.   (adjectives)
The bucket will not fit in the well.   (verb and noun)
The team trained well.   (adverb)

Try it

1 Read the sentence. What type of word is underlined? Write '**noun**', '**verb**' or '**adjective**'.

Ring the door bell of flat one.   _____

She wore a gold ring and a silver watch.   _____

Watch my bag for me and keep it safe.   _____

The man kept the form in the safe.   _____

People began to form a queue.   _____

I had the last slice of cake.   _____

2 Underline the **word** in each sentence that has another meaning. Write a sentence to show the other meaning.

The flames rose into the sky. _____

Joe had a spot on his nose. _____

A feather is really light. _____

Sentence practice

Write a sentence using the word 'wave' as a **verb**. Write another sentence using the word 'wave' as a **noun**.

verb _____

noun _____

Pronouns

Try it

1 Underline all the **pronouns** in each sentence.

The woman saw that we were hungry so she gave us some bread.

The people ran away from the tiger when they saw it coming.

Jack and I said we would help them.

Was Fatima at home when you went to see her?

Max found the book and he gave it to me.

I saw Harry and I spoke to him.

2 Rewrite the sentences using **pronouns** in place of the underlined nouns or noun phrases.

Kofi and I waved to Doug but Doug did not see Kofi and me.

_____

Dad told Mum about the cat but Mum did not believe Dad.

_____

Tia and Shona found a shell and took the shell home with Tia and Shona.

_____

Sentence practice

Write a sentence using the **pronouns** 'he' and 'it'. Make sure it is clear who or what the pronouns refer to.

_____

Pronouns and verbs

Remember

When you use a **pronoun**, you must also use the correct form of the **verb** to follow it.

He <u>is</u> sitting.	He <u>likes</u> this.	He <u>has</u> seen it.
I <u>am</u> sitting.	I <u>like</u> this.	I <u>have</u> seen it.

Try it

1   Write the correct form of the **verb** for each **pronoun**.

I _____ late. They _____ early.   (was were)

She _____ a red flag. I _____ a blue one.   (choose chooses)

He _____ his homework. I _____ mine.   (do does)

We _____ lost. I _____ scared.   (am are is)

They _____ lots of money. He _____ none.   (has have)

I _____ jam and she _____ honey.   (like likes)

2   Rewrite each sentence using the **pronoun** 'I' instead of 'he' or 'she'. Check that you have used the correct form of each **verb**.

He has walked for miles and he is starving.

_____

He does the washing up and he tidies the kitchen.

_____

She's out at the moment but she'll be back soon.

_____

Sentence practice

Write <u>two</u> sentences to describe yourself. Use the correct **verbs** with the **pronoun** 'I'.

_____

Singular and plural nouns

Remember

Most **nouns** are made into **plurals** by adding –s or –es. Sometimes the spelling of the noun changes when you add the plural ending.

lady – ladies

Some plural nouns do not end –s or –es.

man – men   woman – women   child – children

Try it

1 Write the **plural** of these **singular nouns**.

horse	_____	pony	_____
beetle	_____	woodlouse	_____
puppy	_____	kitten	_____
goose	_____	turkey	_____
sheep	_____	fox	_____

2 Rewrite each sentence, making all the **nouns** into **plurals**.

The mouse was eating the berry off the bush.

_____

The witch had a bad foot and a rotten tooth.

_____

Did the deer under the tree have a white patch?

_____

Sentence practice

Write a sentence using the **plural** of the **nouns** 'child', 'jelly', 'party'.

_____

_____

Revision 3

1 Write the underlined words in each sentence as a **contraction** by using an **apostrophe**.

<u>You will</u> never believe what happened.   _____

<u>We are</u> coming to see you on Sunday.   _____

<u>Here is</u> a list of questions.   _____

<u>I have</u> been learning a new song.   _____

2 Rewrite this sentence with the correct **punctuation**.

You will need two ripe peaches a sliced apple some orange segments and a few green grapes.

_____

_____

_____

3 Add the missing **punctuation marks** in each sentence of **direct speech**.

I am so lonely said the little elf.

Help yelled the girl.

I can help you find the key the wizard said.

What is your favourite film asked Shazana.

4 Rewrite each sentence with the correct **punctuation**.

My teachers name is mr andrews. _____

Annies dog is called rex. _____

Is the tigers name maya? _____

Dads new car will come on friday. _____

5 Add the **verbs** needed to complete each sentence below.

I _____ been to school.

Mum _____ been to work.

Now we _____ having tea.

Dad _____ having spaghetti and I _____ having pizza.

He _____ going home and I _____ going shopping.

6 Complete each sentence to say <u>where</u>. Use at least <u>one</u> **preposition** in each sentence.

The pirates buried the treasure _____

Ahmed saw the game he wanted _____

He hid the sack _____

She put the plant _____

7 Add an **adverb** to say <u>when</u> this event happened.

Uncle Colin arrived _____ .

Add an **adverb** to say <u>where</u> the event happened.

Uncle Colin arrived _____ .

8 Add a **subordinate clause** to complete each sentence. Use a different **conjunction** each time.

I packed my bag _____

The car came to a sudden stop _____

He took his umbrella _____

They sat on the river bank _____

Writing task 3

Let's get out of here!

Write part of a story about two characters who find themselves in danger. Use the idea from the picture, or choose one of your own. Your task is to describe the danger and how they get out of it.

Before you start writing, think about:

- what the danger is
- what the children say and do
- how they escape the danger

Use this space to write down some ideas.

Remember

- Write in sentences.
- Use correct punctuation.
- Check your work carefully.

Let's get out of here!

Progress chart

Tick the circle when you can do what the statement says.

Section 1

○ I can punctuate all my sentences with capital letters and full stops.

○ I can write a statement, command, exclamation or question.

○ I can use adjectives to write noun phrases that describe things.

○ I can use 'an' (rather than 'a') before nouns that begin with a vowel sound.

○ I can use commas in between the items in a list.

○ I can use an apostrophe to show that something belongs to someone.

○ I can use –er/–est or 'more'/'most' to form adjectives to compare things.

○ I can use conjunctions to show when and why something happened.

Section 2

○ I can use adverbs to show where, when or how actions are performed.

○ I can use prepositions to show where or when something happened.

○ I can use inverted commas to show the spoken words in direct speech.

○ I can use capital letters, commas, question marks and exclamation marks in direct speech.

○ I can use past tense verbs, including –ing forms.

○ I can use the perfect form of a verb.

○ I can use prefixes and suffixes to make words into nouns.

Section 3

○ I can write sentences using clauses and phrases.

○ I can identify and use subordinate clauses in sentences.

○ I can use paragraphs to group together ideas in my non-fiction writing.

○ I can use adverbs or prepositional phrases at the start of paragraphs when writing stories.

○ I can recognise root words and words from the same word families.

○ I can recognise if a word is a noun, verb, adjective or adverb by looking at how it is used in the sentence.

○ I can identify and use pronouns with the correct verbs.

○ I can use plural nouns that do not end –s/–es.

Glossary

adjective a 'describing word' that tells you more about a noun (e.g. <u>red</u> car)

adverb a word that tells you more about a verb or event (e.g. He walked <u>slowly</u>. I'll go <u>now</u>.)

apostrophe a punctuation mark used in contractions or shortened forms (e.g. can't) or to show that something belongs to someone (e.g. Sam's hat)

clause a group of words that go together and include a verb

comma a punctuation mark used to separate items in a list (,)

command a type of sentence that tells someone to do something (e.g. Stand up.)

conjunction a word that joins together two ideas or two sentences to make one longer sentence (e.g. and, that, because)

consonant the letters b c d f g h j k l m n p q r s t v w x y z

contraction a shortened form of words using an apostrophe in place of missing letters (e.g. don't, I'm)

direct speech writing what someone says using the actual words spoken

exclamation a type of sentence that shows strong feeling, starts with 'What' or 'How' and ends with a verb, followed by an exclamation mark (e.g. What a surprise that was!)

inverted commas/speech marks punctuation marks used to mark the beginning and end of direct speech (" ")

main clause a clause that makes sense on its own (e.g. The girl shouted.)

noun a word that names things (e.g. car, dog, man)

noun phrase a noun and the other words that go with it (e.g. the fast police car with flashing lights)

perfect form a verb form used to refer to events that happened in the past but are still important now (e.g. The tent has started to leak.)

plural more than one of something (e.g. cat<u>s</u>, dog<u>s</u>, fox<u>es</u>, wol<u>ves</u>, child<u>ren</u>)

prefix a group of letters added to the start of a word to make a different word (e.g. <u>un</u>tie, <u>mis</u>take)

preposition a word that shows how something relates to something else in terms of time or place (e.g. in, by, with)

progressive form the –ing verb form used when actions continue for a period of time. It needs the 'helper' verb 'am/are' (e.g. I am sitting, they were singing)

pronoun a word that takes the place of a noun or proper noun (e.g. I, he, we, they)

proper noun the special name of a person, place or thing, which starts with a capital letter (e.g. Jo, Paris, June)

question a type of sentence that asks for information or needs a response, and ends with a question mark (e.g. Who are you?)

root word the base word to which prefixes and suffixes are added (e.g. dis–<u>agree</u>–ment)

singular just one of something (e.g. cat, dog, fox, wolf, child)

statement a type of sentence that gives information or tells you something (e.g. Roses are red.)

subordinate clause a clause that is added to a main clause and does not make sense on its own (e.g. … because she was angry)

suffix a group of letters added to the end of a word to make a different word (e.g. bak<u>er</u>, sad<u>ness</u>)

tense verbs have different tenses that tell you when the action happened – in the present or in the past (e.g. play/played, run/ran)

verb a 'doing word' (e.g. play, run, skip) or 'being word' (e.g. is, was, has, have)

vowel the letters a e i o u

word family words with the same root word that are related by form and meaning (e.g. actor/action/react)

Schofield&Sims

the long-established educational publisher specialising in maths, English and science

Schofield & Sims Grammar and Punctuation is a whole-school scheme that supports a structured approach to teaching and learning these fundamental literacy skills. Comprising six pupil books and six teacher's guides, this comprehensive programme enables pupils to gain a secure understanding of grammar and punctuation as they progress from the identification of individual parts of speech and punctuation marks to the composition of complex multi-clause sentences and paragraphs. Through engaging lessons and practice activities, pupils encounter each grammar point in a range of contexts, enabling them to develop an awareness of the nuances of language and the ability to communicate effectively.

Each pupil book provides:
- full curriculum coverage
- a user-friendly summary of the key learning point for each lesson
- plenty of practice, from short activities that check understanding to more in-depth questions that require pupils to compose their own sentences
- regular revision pages to reinforce learning and identify strengths and weaknesses
- varied writing tasks to promote the application of new knowledge
- a self-evaluation checklist to encourage pupils to assess their own learning
- a glossary to support the confident use of grammatical terminology.

The accompanying teacher's guides contain lesson plans, answers to all the questions in the pupil book, and assessment and record-keeping resources. A selection of free downloads is also available.

Grammar 3 covers the National Curriculum requirements for Year 3, including conjunctions; comparative adjectives; the articles 'a' and 'an'; adverbs; prepositions; direct speech; past and perfect verb forms; main and subordinate clauses; pronouns; nouns with prefixes and suffixes; headings and paragraphs; and word families.

Grammar 1 ISBN 978 07217 1390 8	**Grammar 1 Teacher's Guide**	ISBN 978 07217 1391 5
Grammar 2 ISBN 978 07217 1392 2	**Grammar 2 Teacher's Guide**	ISBN 978 07217 1393 9
Grammar 3 ISBN 978 07217 1394 6	**Grammar 3 Teacher's Guide**	ISBN 978 07217 1395 3
Grammar 4 ISBN 978 07217 1396 0	**Grammar 4 Teacher's Guide**	ISBN 978 07217 1397 7
Grammar 5 ISBN 978 07217 1398 4	**Grammar 5 Teacher's Guide**	ISBN 978 07217 1399 1
Grammar 6 ISBN 978 07217 1400 4	**Grammar 6 Teacher's Guide**	ISBN 978 07217 1401 1

MIX
Paper from
responsible sources
FSC® C023114

ISBN 978-07217-1394-6

9 780721 713946 >

For further information and to place your order visit
www.schofieldandsims.co.uk or telephone 01484 607080

ISBN 978 07217 1394 6
Key Stage 2
Age range 7–9 years
£3.95 (Retail price)